Living History Day

by Kathryn E. Lewis • illustrated by Pamela Johnson

Chapters

Harcourt

Orlando   Boston   Dallas   Chicago   San Diego

Visit *The Learning Site!*

www.harcourtschool.com

A New Project

My problem began the day of the first snowstorm.

Mrs. Parker was doing her best to get our class under control. Still, it was the first snowfall of the year and we were all acting pretty immature.

"Girls and boys! Please. I'd like to discuss an upcoming project with you."

"Mrs. Parker!" Sally Schultz called from the back. "Can't we go outside and catch snowflakes for just a few minutes?"

Sally could barely contain her glee. You would think she had just arrived here from a Polynesian island.

"Sally," Mrs. Parker said, "if you'll let me explain about this new project, I guarantee it will be just as exciting as that new snow out there."

2

We all turned away from the windows. Sitting quietly in our seats, we waited skeptically for Mrs. Parker to continue. After all, what could be more fun than a good old-fashioned snowball fight?

"Thank you," Mrs. Parker said, in her kind, patient voice. "The project is called Living History Day, and the idea is for each of you to "become" someone who has made a significant contribution to our country's history. You can bring in costumes and props, and we'll invite the whole school and all your parents and friends. They'll have an opportunity to talk to each of you about your historical contributions. At the end of the day, a panel of judges will decide which of you best portrayed a distinguished American."

It seemed as if twenty-five hands shot up at the same time, but Mrs. Parker ignored them all and continued to speak.

"For this project to be a success, you should think carefully about the person you want to portray. Try to select someone who made a *significant* contribution to our country. Then find out as much as you can about that person. That way you'll know just what to say when one of our guests asks you a tough question."

"WOW!" Vinnie Simone yelled. "That will be so much fun. Can I be Babe Ruth? He's my hero!"

Rodney Frankel said, "Can I be Elvis Presley? I know all his songs by heart."

Mrs. Parker raised her right eyebrow. Since we all know what that means, the room suddenly became very quiet.

"Thank you," Mrs. Parker said.

Then Mrs. Parker continued with her explanation. "Let me reinforce that you should select someone who really made a difference in the history of our country. I can't stress this enough."

She glanced toward Rodney and Vinnie, and then she swept her eyes around the whole class. "Don't make a hasty choice," she said. "I want you to think about this assignment for a few days before you make your decision. Remember, you are going to spend several weeks studying this person. That is why it is so important that you choose your person carefully."

"Okay," Rodney said, sighing. His sigh could be heard throughout the room. "Maybe I won't be Elvis after all. How about Mickey Mantle or Wilt Chamberlain?"

Mrs. Parker looked at him and shook her head slightly. I thought I saw a smile working at the corners of her mouth.

1. a remarkable American
2. a significant contribution to American history

Then everyone's hands shot up again.

"There are so many great people!" Zoe asked. "How do we go about choosing?" Had Zoe read my mind?

"That's a superb question," Mrs. Parker said. "There are literally thousands of people you could choose. You might choose someone who's alive today, or you might choose someone who lived two hundred years ago. Here's a suggestion. What period of history do you like best? If you like the colonial period, then choose someone who lived then.

"I don't want to be misleading," continued Mrs. Parker. "You can choose whomever you'd find fascinating to study. Here are the only requirements."

Mrs. Parker began to write on the board. When she was finished, she said, "That's it, boys and girls. Why don't you take a few minutes to sit quietly and think about this project."

6

The Big Decision

Over the next few days the classroom was buzzing with excitement. Everyone was so hard at work that Mrs. Parker rarely had to raise her voice above a whisper.

As for me, I was hopelessly stuck. I just couldn't decide which remarkable American I should portray. One minute I was going to be Louis Armstrong, but ten minutes later I imagined myself as President Eisenhower. By the next morning I would wake up and decide that I just *had* to be E.B. White. Yet that night, by dinnertime, I had already gone through Alexander Graham Bell, Charlie Chaplin, and Yogi Berra.

At dinner on Wednesday I explained the problem to my family.

My mother said, "Well, you spend hundreds of hours on the computer. How about portraying Bill Gates?"

Thanks, Mom.

My father said, "You love to eat chocolate. What about Milton Hershey, the man who created the chocolate bar?"

Thanks, Dad.

My younger sister, Leslie, said, "You love to go to amusement parks. What about the person who invented the roller coaster?"

Actually, that wasn't a bad idea. I even looked up the term "roller coaster" in an on-line encyclopedia to see if I could find the name of its inventor.

SIGN-UP
FOR TIME ON THIS COMPUTER
FRIDAY
9:00 - 9:30 — Rosa Parks
9:30 - 10:00 — Ben Franklin
10:00 - 10:30 — Louisa May Alcott
10:30 - 11:00 — Abraham Lincoln
11:00 - 11:30 — Cesar Chavez

By Thursday the assignment had me totally paralyzed. I made list after list of possible choices. I made one list of my favorite authors and another list of my favorite Presidents. On Wednesday night I was sure I was going to be Davy Crockett. I listed all the neat things he had done and why he was the perfect choice. After all, he had been a frontier hero, a pioneer, and a famous politician. The next morning, I woke up remembering that I had dreamed about becoming Teddy Roosevelt. He was a soldier, a President, a boxer, and a hunter. He even had the teddy bear named after him!

Every time I thought I had made up my mind, another, more remarkable, American popped into it. Class time was pure torture. Everyone was hard at work learning about his or her person.

8

There were biographies and articles scattered all over the room. The sign-up sheets for the two classroom computers were filled with famous names.

How should I sign up, "I.M. Confused"?

By Friday I was in such a panic that I was too embarrassed to even ask Mrs. Parker for help. At one point she passed my desk and spotted me reading a magazine article about Frank Lloyd Wright, the famous architect. He was one of my father's helpful suggestions.

Mrs. Parker said, "Peter, I didn't know you had chosen Frank Lloyd Wright. He would be a fascinating person to study, but don't I have you listed as Davy Crockett?"

"I'm just not sure," I said. "Is it too late to change my mind?"

"Well," Mrs. Parker looked at me kindly and said, "Monday is the deadline. Can I help you make your decision?"

"Thanks, but no problem," I said hopefully. "I'll know for sure by Monday." Just then the bell rang and I hurried out of the classroom.

At home I collapsed onto the living room couch. What was I going to do? At that precise moment, I glanced across the room at the framed photograph of my great-great-grandfather and my eyes looked into his eyes. I'm not kidding about this; I felt that he was trying to communicate something to me.

Then I knew exactly who I was going to be on Living History Day. I felt indebted forever to a man I had never met.

Come to
Living History Day
Meet some
remarkable Americans!
Join us in the
Baker School Gym
this Friday
from 1 to 4

Final Preparations

All the invitations had been sent. We were busy transforming the school gym into the Living History Museum. I was painting an enormous mural of a mountain scene. Alex Lucas was at the desk next to mine. As he walked by my desk, Alex, who was going to be Thomas Jefferson, looked into my duffel bag and said, "Hey, Peter. What's with the train tracks? Who did you *finally* decide to be? A train conductor?" He made a noise like a train whistle and started to laugh.

Alexis Carra, who was going to be Betsy Ross, was busy painting an American flag on a giant sheet of cardboard. At the sound of the laughter, she looked up and said, "Hey, Peter, this is supposed to be a serious project. Who said you could bring in your favorite toys? Who are you going to be, Santa Claus?"

10

I was too busy painting my mountain to be distracted and since I had started late, I had a lot to get done in a short amount of time. At lunchtime my dad brought in a large piece of plywood on which I had painted a rural scene. Mrs. Parker helped us push four desks together and lay the plywood on top of the desks. I started to place the train tracks on the sheet of plywood.

"Hey, Peter," said Ben Dazzi. "What's with the train tracks? Who did you ever decide to be? I'm going to be Meriwether Lewis, the famous explorer. Want to take me for a train ride?" He snickered as he walked away.

Living History Day

The big day was finally here. The transformation of the gym was complete. Tables and chairs were set up along the walls, and behind each table a large display board had been hung. No one would ever have believed that this well-organized space was usually the setting for wild and noisy games of basketball.

Just before noon we all hurried to get into our costumes and scrambled to get to our tables. At exactly one o'clock, the gym doors were opened and a horde of students, parents, and other visitors rushed in.

I am not kidding about this. You could see the utter amazement on everyone's faces. You could practically hear the group's "WOW" as people looked around.

Dressed in our costumes, surrounded by our props, each remarkable American was seated next to his or her special display.

"This is terrific," I heard one parent saying to another. "I don't know which of these amazing people to talk to first. Look, there's Ben Franklin next to Dr. Martin Luther King. There's Susan B. Anthony sitting beside Dr. Jonas Salk. Where should we begin?"

History Day

I was too busy to notice where the judges were. People of all ages were crowded around my display, looking at the trains as they whizzed along the tracks, and asking me a million questions.

The next thing I knew, the three judges had wandered over to our side of the gymnasium. One, a sixth-grade teacher named Mr. Kaplan, had started a conversation with Juan Ramirez. Dressed in an old-fashioned suit, Juan was spending the afternoon as the African American composer Scott Joplin. His display included a miniature piano and a tape recorder that was playing Scott Joplin's jaunty ragtime music.

"Mr. Joplin, I just love your music!" said Mr. Kaplan. "Which of your compositions is your favorite?"

"Thanks for a question that doesn't stump me!" Juan replied. " 'Maple Leaf Rag' is my favorite. It's also one of my best known. Still, the truth is that I didn't gain real recognition until after my death. In 1976 I won a Pulitzer Prize."

"Thanks for sharing that fascinating information," Mr. Kaplan said as he waved goodbye and wandered over to talk to the photographer Dorothea Lange.

Abigail Feinstein was Dorothea Lange for the afternoon. She had a camera around her neck and a display of her documentary photographs. Mr. Kaplan studied the photos carefully before he began to speak.

Meanwhile I could hear Mrs. Lambert, another judge, talking to Bernie Peterson. As Cesar Chavez, he was explaining when he had begun to organize the migrant workers in California. Next to him were Zoe Johnstone as Susan B. Anthony, the famous women's suffrage leader, and Jimmy Martinez as Francis Scott Key, the lawyer who wrote the lyrics for our national anthem. At another table, Emma and Chloe Fast, our class twins, were dramatizing a pair of remarkable women—Helen Keller and her tutor and interpreter Anne Sullivan.

The day went by in a flash. Suddenly Mrs. Parker stepped up to a makeshift podium and said, "Thank you all for coming. We hope all of you have had as much fun and learned as much as we have. There is just one last thing to be done before we bring this fascinating afternoon to a close."

Before I knew what was happening, all three judges were standing next to my table. Mr. Kaplan taped an award onto my display and said, "Peter, you have accomplished something very important here today. You have taught us that it is not just famous Americans who have made significant contributions to our history. You have reminded us that, without the hard work of each and every American, our great country would not be what it is today. Thank you, Peter."

Everyone around me was applauding. I could see tears on my mother's face and joy in my father's eyes.

Have you already figured out the identity of my remarkable American? If you have, congratulations! If you haven't, here's how I introduced him to my visitors.

"My name is Peter Chen. I was born in 1845 in a small village in northern China. Despite my parents' pleas, I decided to leave China and seek my freedom in a new and different place. I had no money. The only way I could get to America was to sign a contract forcing me to work for four years in exchange for wages and free passage on a ship.

"After a long, hard voyage, we came ashore in San Francisco, California. The year was 1865. I didn't speak one word of English. I was immediately transported into the countryside, where I was given a sledgehammer and told to get to work. Mile by mile, driving spike after spike into the steel rails, I helped build the first transcontinental railroad in the United States. I hammered my way into American history.

"The history of our country was changed forever by the sweat and toil of laborers like me. When you talk about our country's history, please, please, don't forget people like us.

"Oh, by the way, do you know the thoughtful, intelligent boy in your class with a name exactly like mine? He happens to be my great-great-grandson."